SO-AEU-834

WARRIORS

TIGERSTAR & SASHA

#1: INTO THE WOODS

TIGERSTAR & SASHA
#1: INTO THE WOODS

CREATED BY
ERIN HUNTER

WRITTEN BY
DAN JOLLEY

ART BY
DON HUDSON

HAMBURG // LONDON // LOS ANGELES // TOKYO

HarperCollinsPublishers

Warriors: Tigerstar and Sasha Vol. 1:
Into the Woods
Created by Erin Hunter
Written by Dan Jolley
Art by Don Hudson

Cover Colorist - Jason Van Winkle
Digital Tones - Lincy Chan
Lettering - Lucas Rivera
Cover Design - Tina Corrales

Editor - Lillian Diaz-Przybyl
Digital Imaging Manager - Chris Buford
Pre-Production Supervisor - Lucas Rivera
Managing Editor - Vy Nguyen
Creative Director - Anne Marie Horne
Editor-in-Chief - Rob Tokar
Publisher - Mike Kiley
President and C.O.O. - John Parker
C.E.O. and Chief Creative Officer - Stu Levy

A Manga

TOKYOPOP and the robot icon are trademarks or registered trademarks of TOKYOPOP Inc.

TOKYOPOP Inc.
5900 Wilshire Blvd. Suite 2000
Los Angeles, CA 90036

E-mail: info@TOKYOPOP.com
Come visit us online at www.TOKYOPOP.com

For information address HarperCollins Children's Books, a division of HarperCollins Publishers,
10 East 53rd Street, New York, NY 10022
www.harpercollinschildrens.com

ISBN 978-0-06-154792-8
Library of Congress catalog card number: 2007909574

13 LP/ BVG 10 9 8 7
❖
First Edition

Dear readers,

I was always fascinated by the idea of Tigerstar befriending a loner like Sasha. After all, he declared himself the sworn enemy of any cat who lived outside the Clans. When we met Sasha, she revealed herself to be a proud, independent cat who had enough respect for Clan values to want her kits to be raised as warriors. What did she see in Tigerstar? He may have been a great warrior—fearless, strong, and farsighted in planning his march to leadership—but he was hardly a romantic hero. And to make things even more mysterious, Sasha obviously knew the horror that Tigerstar had brought to the forest because she made her kits promise not to tell their new Clanmates who their father was; she didn't want her children to grow up with their father's reputation hanging over their heads.

But Sasha also raised Hawkfrost and Mothwing to have respect for Tigerstar's strengths—his courage, his sense of pride and ambition, and his willingness to fight for what he believed in. So Sasha must have genuinely loved the cat who murdered and lied his way to leadership, and who nearly destroyed all the Clans when he tried to manipulate Scourge into allying with him. What happened when she met him? How long was it before she saw his true colors? What made her leave her beloved kits in RiverClan?

It's time for Sasha to tell her story. . . .

Best wishes always,
Erin Hunter

WELL, IF THERE ARE CLAN CATS AROUND HERE, I WANT TO SEE THEM.

AND I'M PLENTY PATIENT. I'LL WAIT AS LONG AS I HAVE TO.

WHAT A TERRIBLE NIGHT.

MAYBE THIS WAS A STUPID IDEA. MAYBE NOBODY SEES THESE CLAN CATS. MAYBE THEY'RE NOT REAL.

MAYBE THEY'RE—OH!

...D THAT'S WHERE IT ...AN. WE MET AGAIN ...HE NEXT NIGHT...

...AND THE NEXT...

...AND THE NEXT.

NIGHT AFTER NIGHT, JUST THE TWO OF US. TIGERSTAR IS SO POLITE, AND STRONG, AND...

...HE MAKES ME FEEL SO SAFE. I LOVE THAT.

DO I--AM I--AM I FALLING IN LOVE WITH HIM? IS THAT WHAT THIS FEELING IS, IN MY HEART?

IT'S NOT LONG BEFORE TIGERSTAR STARTS TELLING ME ABOUT WHAT IT'S LIKE TO BE PART OF SHADOWCLAN.

EVERY NIGHT, WHEN HE COMES TO SEE ME, HE TELLS ME ABOUT CLAN LIFE, AND THE WARRIOR CODE.

AND ONE NIGHT WHEN THERE ARE NO CLOUDS IN THE SKY AT ALL...

...HE TELLS ME ABOUT STARCLAN.

I NEVER THOUGHT IT COULD HAPPEN, BUT I'M STARTING TO THINK I COULD BE HAPPY HERE. HERE...WITH TIGERSTAR.

WHERE IS HE, ANYWAY?

I HOPE HE'S OKAY. IF ANYTHING HAPPENED TO HIM...WELL, I DON'T WANT TO THINK ABOUT IT.

GUESS I'LL JUST GET SOMETHING TO EAT AND HEAD HOME.

EVENING, SASHA.

THERE YOU ARE!

WHAT HAPPENED? WHERE WERE YOU?

I WAS WORRIED SICK!

IT STARTED RAINING THE MORNING AFTER TIGERSTAR AND I FOUGHT.

IT HASN'T STOPPED FOR DAYS.

WITH ALL THIS TIME TO THINK, I CAN'T HELP BUT WONDER...

PREY'S GETTING SCARCER. MY STOMACH WON'T STOP GROWLING.

MAYBE TIGERSTAR'S RIGHT.

MAYBE I AM A KITTYPET AT HEART.

WHAMM

RRHHRRRHHH!

GET OUT OF HERE! NOW.

TIGERSTAR! HOW--?

I HAVE TO GET BACK TO THE CAMP NOW.

THANK YOU AGAIN FOR HELPING ME.

I'LL BE PATROLLING TONIGHT.

CAN I SEE YOU AGAIN?

WHAT, EVEN THOUGH I'M A KITTYPET?

YOU'RE NOT. NOT REALLY. YOU'RE A... ROGUE.

IF YOU EVER GET CAUGHT BY A CLAN CAT, YOU MUST TELL THEM THAT. PROMISE?

WHY DO YOU HAVE TO GIVE EVERY CAT A NAME? WHY CAN'T WE JUST ALL BE CATS?

BECAUSE IT DOESN'T WORK THAT WAY.

IF YOU WERE BORN IN THE FOREST, YOU'D UNDERSTAND.

I THINK ABOUT WHAT TIGERSTAR SAID ALL DAY. CLANS...ROGUES...KITTYPETS.

I DON'T SEE WHY WE CAN'T ALL JUST LIVE AND LET LIVE.

CONFUSED OR NOT, THOUGH, I HAVE MORE RESPECT FOR CLAN CATS NOW.

I CAN'T SEE SHNUKY EVER TAKING ON ONE FOX, NEVER MIND TWO.

TIGERSTAR...?

HERE.

SASHA, ARE YOU CRAZY? WHAT ARE YOU DOING WITH HIM?

THERE'S NO NEED TO BE SCARED. HIS NAME IS TIGERSTAR. HE SAVED MY LIFE.

OH, SASHA... YOU LOVE HIM, DON'T YOU? YOU LOVE THAT WILD CAT! I CAN TELL!

IT'S--I'M...I'M LONELY WITHOUT MY HOUSEFOLK.

BUT CATS LIKE US AND FOREST CATS DON'T MIX! EVERYBODY KNOWS THAT!

ENOUGH TALK. WE NEED TO GO.

SHNUKY DOESN'T UNDERSTAND. MY LIFE IS DIFFERENT NOW. I'M NOT A KITTYPET ANYMORE.

I DECIDE RIGHT THEN AND THERE: I'M GOING WITH TIGERSTAR TO THE FOREST, AND I'M NOT COMING BACK HERE.

EVER.

61

THIS IS THE WARRIORS' DEN. IT'S A GREAT HONOR TO SLEEP HERE, AMONG THOSE CATS WHO DEFEND SHADOWCLAN WITH THEIR LIVES.

AND THIS IS ONE OF MY FINEST FIGHTERS: BOULDER.

PLEASED TO MEET YOU.

HI!

THIS IS THE DEN WHERE OUR MEDICINE CAT LIVES AND WORKS.

HIS NAME IS RUNNINGNOSE.

I'M CONCENTRATING HERE! UNLESS ONE OF YOU IS SICK, PLEASE COME BACK ANOTHER TIME!

AND THE BIGGEST SURPRISE IS YET TO COME.

SASHA. WE'RE PUTTING TOGETHER A HUNTING PARTY.

CARE TO JOIN US?

OW CAN SAY NO?

THE PARTY'S MADE UP OF BLACKFOOT (THE CLAN DEPUTY), RUSSETFUR, JAGGEDTOOTH, ROWANPAW...AND ME.

I'M NERVOUS BEYOND BELIEF AT FIRST...

...BUT THEN RUSSETFUR TELLS ME SOMETHING THAT REALLY HELPS.

DON'T WORRY, SASHA. BLACKFOOT, JAGGEDTOOTH, AND I ALL USED TO BE ROGUES. JUST LIKE YOU.

I LIKE RUSSETFUR A LOT ALREADY.

WE STOP CHATTING ONCE THINGS GET DOWN TO BUSINESS.

OH, NO YOU DON'T!

GOTCHA!

WOW! I'VE NEVER SEEN ANYBODY CLIMB A TREE SO FAST! HOW'D YOU GET SO GOOD?

WELL, I'VE HAD A LOT OF PRACTICE--

I BREAK OFF MY WORDS. I WAS ABOUT TO SAY, "CLIMBING FENCES." TIGERSTAR WOULD'VE BEEN SO MAD AT ME!

IT'S A FANTASTIC FEELING WHEN WE COME BACK TO CAMP, BRINGING FOOD FOR REST OF THE CLAN.

I CAN TELL TIGERSTAR'S PLEASED. THAT LOOK HE GIVES ME...IT JUST MAKES ME GET ALL MELTY.

WELL DONE.

IT'S GETTING LATE, AND THE AIR IS COOL TONIGHT. WOULD YOU LIKE TO SLEEP IN THE WARRIORS' DEN?

HUH? ...ARE YOU SERIOUS?

TIGERSTAR'S RIGHT. THE NIGHTS ARE GETTING COLDER. LEAF-BARE ISN'T TOO FAR AWAY.

BUT TONIGHT...I'M AS WARM AS IF I'D BEEN SLEEPING IN A SUNBEAM.

TIGERSTAR INVITES ME TO GO ON PATROL WITH HIM THE NEXT MORNING...HIM AND OAKFUR AND BOULDER.

I'M REALLY ENJOYING MYSELF IN SHADOWCLAN, SO I ACCEPT IMMEDIATELY.

WE'RE ABOUT HALFWAY THROUGH THE PATROL ROUTE WHEN WE PASS BY THE THUNDERPATH.

THEY TELL ME HOW THIS IS THE BORDER BETWEEN SHADOWCLAN'S TERRITORY AND THUNDERCLAN'S.

BUT SOON IT LOOKS AS THOUGH SOME CATS PAY MORE ATTENTION TO BORDERS THAN OTHERS.

HMMM...YOUNG THUNDERCLAN WARRIORS, ON SHADOWCLAN LAND.

HOW CARELESS OF THEM.

HEY--HEY! LOOK AT THAT!

TRAITOR!

YOU'LL PAY FOR WHAT YOU DID TO THUNDERCLAN!

TIGERSTAR? WHY ARE THEY CALLING YOU A TRAITOR?

I KNEW I'D HAVE TO EXPLAIN THIS EVENTUALLY. I WAS ONCE DEPUTY OF THUNDERCLAN.

I WAS DRIVEN OUT THEIR FORMER LEADER, BLUESTAR, WHO WAS [W]AK AND ENVIOUS OF MY STRENGTH.

NOW THEY'RE LED BY FIRESTAR, AND THEY'RE A MENACE TO THE FOREST. THEY PAY NO REGARD TO THE WARRIOR CODE.

BETWEEN YOU AND ME, I'M WORRIED THAT FIRESTAR HAS AMBITIONS TO RULE THE ENTIRE FOREST.

PART OF ME DOESN'T WANT TO GO...BUT I KNOW I SHOULD GET BACK TO MY OWN DEN FOR A WHILE.

THANK YOU FOR A LOVELY TIME, TIGERSTAR.

SASHA...WILL YOU JOIN US? JOIN THE CLAN?

YOU'D FIT IN WELL. YOU CAN HUNT. YOU'RE A GOOD FIGHTER.

JOIN SHADOWCLAN...! THAT WOULD BE SO GREAT! BUT–BUT WHAT IF KEN CAME BACK?

CAN I THINK ABOUT IT?

I'LL COME TO YOUR DEN TOMORROW NIGHT. YOU CAN TELL ME THEN.

TOMORROW NIGHT...? WHY SO FAST?

OKAY...

OKAY. THAT DOES IT. IF THAT'S WHAT I'VE GOT TO LOOK FORWARD TO AS A ROGUE...THEN I'LL DO IT.

TIGERSTAR'S GOING TO BE SO HAPPY!

I'LL JOIN SHADOWCLAN!

OH--I CAN HEAR VOICES UP AHEAD. DON'T WANT TO DISTURB ANYBODY. AFTER ALL, I'M NOT A CLAN MEMBER YET.

WAIT...IS THAT TIGERSTAR'S VOICE?

To Be Continue

ERIN HUNTER

is inspired by a love of cats and a fascination with the ferocity of the natural world. As well as having great respect for nature in all its forms, Erin enjoys creating rich mythical explanations for animal behavior, shaped by her interest in astrology and standing stones. She is also the author of the Seekers series.

Visit the Clans online
and play the Warriors Quest game at
www.warriorcats.com.

For exclusive information on your
favorite authors and artists, visit
www.authortracker.com.

The #1 national bestselling series, now in manga!

WARRIORS

TIGERSTAR & SASHA

TOKYOPOP

ESCAPE FROM THE FOREST

HARPER COLLINS

ERIN HUNTER

2

WARRIORS

THE RISE OF SCOURGE

TOKYOPOP®

HARPER COLLINS

ERIN HUNTER

WARRIORS

THE RISE OF
SCOURGE

Black-and-white Tiny may be the runt of the litter, but he's also the most curious about what lies beyond the backyard fence. When he crosses paths with some wild cats defending their territory, Tiny is left with scars— and a bitter, deep-seated grudge—that he carries with him back to Twolegplace. As his reputation grows among the strays and loners that live in the dirty brick alleyways, Tiny leaves behind his name, his kittypet past, and everything that was once important to him— except his deadly desire for revenge.

WARRIORS
CATS of the CLANS

ERIN HUNTER
ILLUSTRATED BY WAYNE McLOUGHLIN

MEET THE CLANS' HEROES IN

WARRIORS

CATS of the CLANS

Hear the stories of the great warriors as they've never
been told before! Chock-full of visual treats and cap-
tivating details, including full-color illustrations and
in-depth biographies of important cats from all four
Clans, from fierce Clan leaders to wise medicine cats
to the most mischievous kits.

POWER OF THREE

WARRIORS

ECLIPSE

ERIN HUNTER

POWER OF THREE

WARRIORS

BOOK 4:
ECLIPSE

TURN THE PAGE FOR A PEEK
AT THE NEXT WARRIORS NOVEL,
*WARRIORS: POWER OF THREE
#4: ECLIPSE.*

Firestar's grandchildren have learned of the powerful prophecy that foretells their destinies, and the responsibility of deciding the Clans' future weighs heavily on the three apprentices. Each secretly yearns for power, and their strengths are tested when ThunderClan is suddenly attacked—and all the Clans are thrown into a battle unlike any the cats have seen.

Jaypaw touched his nose to Tawnypelt's pad. It felt hot and fat. "Swollen," he pronounced. "The skin's grazed but not bleeding. But you already know that." He could hear Hollypaw and Lionpaw's faint mews as they headed away to find prey. Were they talking about the prophecy?

Tawnypelt pulled her paw from under his muzzle. "I knew I couldn't taste blood but I wasn't sure if a stone had worked its way in." She licked it. "My pads have grown so hard from the mountains, I can't tell calluses from cuts anymore."

"No stones," Jaypaw reassured her. He nodded toward the sound of water babbling over rocks nearby. "That stream doesn't sound too deep. Go stand in it. The cold water should ease the swelling."

He padded after her and heard the splash as she leaped into the water.

"It's cold!" she gasped.

"Good," he mewed. "It'll take down the swelling quicker." He pricked his ears. Hollypaw and Lionpaw's voices had faded into the distance. He had shared with them the secret he had carried with him for so long. Telling it had felt like walking through unknown territory, each word falling like a paw step on uncertain ground. Lionpaw had accepted it as though something that had been confusing him had finally been explained. Hollypaw's reaction had been more frustrating: She seemed only concerned about how they could use their powers to help ThunderClan, and kept fretting about the warrior code. Didn't she understand that the prophecy meant more than that? They had been given a power that stretched far beyond the boundaries set by ordinary cats.

Tawnypelt's mew interrupted his thoughts. "This water's *very* cold."

"It's mountain water."

"I can tell," Tawnypelt meowed urgently. "My paws have gone numb!"

"Well, get out then."

With a sigh of relief, she landed beside him and began shaking the water from her paws, scattering icy drops on his fur.

Jaypaw shivered and moved away; mountain winds and cold water were a bad mix. "Does it still hurt?"

"I can't feel it at all," Tawnypelt replied. She paused. "Actually, I can't feel any of my paws."

Squirrelflight was padding toward them. "Any better?"

"I think so," Tawnypelt meowed uncertainly.

Jaypaw felt his mother's tongue lap his ear. "Are you okay, little one?" she asked gently.

He ducked away crossly. "Why shouldn't I be?"

"It's okay to be tired." Squirrelflight sat down. "It's been a hard journey."

"I'm fine," Jaypaw snapped. His mother's tail was twitching, scraping the gritty rock. He waited for her to make some comment about how much harder the journey must have been for him, being blind and all, and then add some mouse-brained comment about how well he had coped with the unfamiliar territory.

"All three of you have been quiet since the battle," she ventured.

She's worried about all of us! Jaypaw's anger melted. He wished he could put her mind at rest but there was no way he could tell her the huge secret that was occupying their thoughts. "I guess we just want to get home," he offered.

"We all do." Squirrelflight rested her chin on top of Jaypaw's head and he pressed against her, suddenly feeling like a kit again, grateful for her warmth.

"They're back!"

At Tawnypelt's call, Squirrelflight jerked away.

Jaypaw lifted his nose and smelled Hollypaw and Lionpaw. He heard claws scrabbling over rock as Breezepaw arrived. The hunters had returned.

"Let's see what they've caught!" Tawnypelt hurried to greet the apprentices.

Jaypaw already knew what they'd caught. His belly rumbled as he padded after her, the mouthwatering smells of squirrel, rabbit, and pigeon filling his nose. If only it weren't going to be given to the Tribe.

Crowfeather and Brambleclaw were already clustered around the makeshift fresh-kill pile. Stormfur and Brook hung back as though embarrassed by the gift.

"This rabbit's so fat it'll feed all the to-bes," Squirrel-flight mewed admiringly.

"Well caught, Breezepaw," Tawnypelt purred.

Jaypaw waited for the WindClan apprentice's pelt to flash with pride, but instead he sensed anxiety claw at Breezepaw. *He's waiting for his father to praise him.*

"Nice pigeon," Crowfeather mewed to Lionpaw.

Breezepaw stiffened with anger.

"And look at the squirrel I caught!" Hollypaw chipped in. "Did you ever see such a juicy one?"

"Come see!" Tawnypelt called to Stormfur and Brook.

The two warriors padded over.

"This will be very welcome," Stormfur meowed formally.

"The Tribe thanks you." Brook's mew was taut.

Jaypaw understood their unease. By accepting fresh-kill, they were openly admitting their weakness. Hunting was poor in the mountains now that two groups of cats were sharing the territory. And yet Jaypaw could feel fierce pride pulsing from Stormfur. *The mountain breeze stirs his heart as well as his pelt.* There was a core of strength within him, a resolve that Jaypaw had not sensed before, as though he were more rooted in the crags and ravines than he ever had been beside the lake. *He truly believes that this is his destiny.* The Tribe were Stormfur's Clan now. He had been born River-Clan, and lived with ThunderClan, but now it seemed that he had found his true home.

Jaypaw shivered. The wind had been sharpened by a late-afternoon chill.

A howl echoed from the slopes far above.

Brook bristled. "Wolves."

"We'll get this prey home safely," Stormfur reassured her. "The wolves are too clumsy to follow our mountain paths."

"But there's a lot of open territory before you reach them," Brambleclaw urged. "You should go."

"We should all head home," Crowfeather advised. "The smell of this fresh-kill will be attracting all the prey-eaters around here."

Alarm flashed from every pelt as Jaypaw detected a strange tang on the breeze. It was the first wolf scent he'd smelled. It reminded him of the dogs around the Twoleg farm, but there was a rawness to it, a scent of blood and flesh that the dogs did not carry. He was thankful it was faint. "They're a long way off," he murmured.

"But they travel fast," Brook warned. The rabbit's fur brushed the ground as she picked it up.

"We're going to miss you," Squirrelflight meowed. Her voice was thick with sadness.

Brook laid the rabbit down again, a purr rising in her

throat. Her pelt brushed Squirrelflight's. "Thank you for taking us in and showing us such kindness."

"ThunderClan is grateful for your loyalty and courage," Brambleclaw meowed.

"We'll see you again, though, won't we?" Hollypaw mewed hopefully.

Jaypaw wondered if he would ever return to the mountains. Would he meet the Tribe of Endless Hunting again? He had followed Stoneteller into his dreams and been led by the Tribe-healer's ancestor to the hollow where ranks of starry cats encircled a shimmering pool. He shivered as he recalled their words: *You have come.* They had been expecting him, and they had known about the prophecy! Yet again, Jaypaw wondered where the prophecy had come from, and how the Tribe of Endless Hunting were connected to his own ancestors.

"There's no more time for good-byes!" Crowfeather's mew was impatient.

"Take care, little one." Brook's cheek brushed Jaypaw's before she turned to say good-bye to Hollypaw.

Stormfur licked his ear. "Look after your brother and sister," he murmured.

"Bye, Stormfur." Jaypaw's throat tightened. "Good-bye, Brook." He remembered the times when Brook had comforted and encouraged him. She had always seemed to understand what it felt like to be different. And Stormfur had never patronized him, but treated him with the same warmth and strictness as he had the other apprentices. He would miss them.

Lionpaw pushed in front of him. "Good-bye, Stormfur. Show those invaders that a Clan cat is never beaten."

"Good-bye, Lionpaw," Stormfur meowed. "Remember that even though our experiences change us, we have to carry on."

A rush of warmth seemed to flood between the warrior and apprentice, and Jaypaw realized with surprise that his brother shared a special bond with Stormfur, one he had not detected before. He stood wondering about it as his Clanmates began to head off down the slope, not moving when Stormfur picked up the freshly caught prey and started uphill after his mate.

"Stop dawdling!" Crowfeather nudged Jaypaw with his nose, steering him down a smooth rocky slope onto the grassy hillside.

Jaypaw bristled. "I don't need help!"

"Please yourself," Crowfeather hissed. "But don't blame me if you get left behind." He pounded ahead, his paws thrumming on the ground.

Imagine having such a sour-tongued warrior for a father. I'm glad I'm not Breezepaw!

"Hurry up, Jaypaw!" Lionpaw was calling.

Jaypaw sniffed the air. On this exposed slope it was easy to tell where the other cats were. Brambleclaw led the way downhill, Breezepaw at his heels, while Crowfeather had already caught up and was flanking Tawnypelt, keeping to the outside of the group. Squirrelflight padded alone, while Hollypaw and Lionpaw trotted behind.

Jaypaw raced after them. The grass was smooth and soft beneath his paws. "It feels strange leaving them behind," he panted.

"They chose to stay," Crowfeather pointed out.

"Do you think we'll ever see them or the Tribe again?" Tawnypelt wondered.

"I hope not," Crowfeather answered. "I don't want to see those mountains once more as long as I live."

"They might visit the lake," Hollypaw suggested.

A howl echoed eerily around the crags far behind them.

"They have to get home safely first," Lionpaw murmured.

"They will," Brambleclaw assured him. "They know their territory as well as any other Tribe cat."

Padding beside his littermates, Jaypaw caught the musty scent of forest ahead. Before long the ground beneath his paws turned from grass to crushed leaves. The wind ceased tugging at his fur as trees shielded him on every side. Hollypaw hurried ahead as though she already scented the lake beyond, but for a moment Jaypaw wished he were back on the open slopes of the foothills. At least there, scents and sounds were not muffled by the enclosing trees, and there was no undergrowth to trip him up. He felt blinder here in this unfamiliar forest than he ever had.

"Watch out!" Lionpaw's warning came too late, and Jaypaw found his paws tangled in a bramble.

"Mouse dung!" He fought to free himself, but the bramble seemed to twist around his legs as if it meant to ensnare him.

"Stand still!" Hollypaw was racing back to help. Jaypaw froze, swallowing his frustration, and allowed Lionpaw to drag the tendrils from around his paws while Hollypaw gently guided him away from the prickly bush.

"Dumb brambles!" Jaypaw lifted his chin and padded forward, more unsure than ever of the terrain but trying desperately not to show it.

Wordlessly, Hollypaw and Lionpaw fell into step on either side of him. With the lightest touch of her whiskers Hollypaw guided him around a clump of nettles and, when a fallen tree blocked their path, Lionpaw warned him with a flick of his tail to stop and wait while he led the way up and over the trunk.

As Jaypaw scrabbled gratefully over the crumbling bark he couldn't help wondering: *Is the prophecy really meant for a cat who can't see?*